Dear Dad

from you to me®

from you to me®

concept by Neil Coxon

Dear Dad

from you to me®

This book is for your Father's unique story.

It is for him to capture some of his life's key memories, experiences and feelings.

Ask him to complete it carefully and, if he wants to, add some photographs or images to personalise it more.

When it is finished and returned to you, this will be a record of his story . . . a story that you will treasure forever.

Dear Dad

Here is a gift from me to you . . . for you to give to me.

When we are children we are always asking questions . . . well I now have some more for you.

Please could you answer them in the way that only you know how and then give the book back to me.

There might be a couple of questions that you prefer not to answer, so don't worry, just answer the others as well as you can . . . I won't mind.

People say that we all have at least one book in us, and this will be one of yours.

The story of you and me that I will treasure forever.

Thank you,

with love

Louise
x

Tell me about the time and place you were born . . .

What are your **earliest** memories?

Tell me about your Mum and Dad ...

What do you think your parents thought of you
as a child?

What **interesting** information do you know about other people in our family?

Please detail what you know of our family tree...

Here's some space for you to add more about our family that will interest generations to come . . .

What do you remember about the place/s you lived when you were a child?

What were your favourite childhood toys or games?

Tell me about your **best friend**/s as a young child . . .

What do you remember about your holidays as a child?

What sort of pets did you have when you were young and what were their names?

What were you best at when you were at school?

What did you want to do when you grew up?

Who was your **best friend** as a teenager . . . and why?

What were your favourite hobbies when you were young?

Did you have an idol when you were young?
Tell me who and why . . .

What was the first piece of music you bought?

What piece/s of music would you choose in your own favourite 'top 10' from when you were young?

Describe any family **traditions** you had or maybe still have . . .

What age were you when you started work?

Tell me about the jobs you have had . . .

What was the first car you owned?

Tell me about the other vehicles you have had . . .

How did you meet my Mother?

What would you do for a **night-out** when you were **dating**?

Tell me about a special piece of music that you and Mum had 'just for you' …

How long had you **known** my **Mother** when you decided to have children?

How did you feel when you found out you were going to be a father?

What did you **think** when you first saw me **after** I was born?

What were my **statistics** when I was **born** . . .
time of birth, weight, height etc?

What did I **look like** when I was born?
If you have a photo, could you stick it here please . . .

What was my **nickname** before I was born or when I was young?

Before I was born, what other names had you thought of calling me? thought of calling me?

What was the **first word** or **words** you remember me saying?

Describe some of the favourite memories you
have of me when I was a child . . .

What was I like when I was a child?

What **attributes** did I have as a child that I still have now?

What were you most proud of about me when
I was at school?

Describe what you like about me . . .

Is there anything you would like to change about me?

What are the happiest or greatest memories of your life?

What are a few of your **favourite** things?

Tell me about the things that make you laugh ...

Describe your memory of some major world events that have happened in your lifetime . . .

Describe the greatest change that you have seen in your lifetime so far . . .

Describe something you still want to achieve in your life . . .

Tell me about the dreams you have for your life . . .

If you were an **animal** . . . what **type** of animal would you be, and why?

If you won the Lottery . . . what would you do with the money?

What have you found most difficult in your life?

What is your **biggest regret** in your life?

Can you do anything about it **now**?

With hindsight what would you do **differently**?

Tell me something you think I won't know about you . . .

What would you like your epitaph to say?

Is there anything you would like to say **sorry** for?

What piece of **advice** would you like to **offer** me?

And now your chance to write **anything** else you want to say to me . . .

These extra pages are for us to write any
questions, memories or **answers** that
may not have been covered elsewhere in the book . . .

And finally for the record . . .

what is your full name ?

what is your date of birth ?

what colour are your eyes ?

how tall are you ?

what blood group are you ?

what was the date when you completed this story for me ?

Dear

I will treasure this book, your memories and your advice forever.

I hope you enjoyed answering my questions.

Thank you so much for doing it and for writing your own book about you and me . . .

from you to me

Dear Dad

from you to me®

First published in the UK by *from you to me*, April 2007
Version 2 - August 2008
Copyright, *from you to me* limited 2007/8
Hackless House, Murhill, Bath, BA2 7FH
www.fromyoutome.com
E-mail: hello@fromyoutome.com

ISBN 978-1-907048-01-2

Cover design by so design consultants, Wick, Bristol, UK
Printed and bound in the UK by CPI William Clowes, Beccles

This paper is manufactured from material sourced from forests certified according to strict environmental, social and economical standards.

If you think other questions should be included in future editions, please let us know. And please share some of the interesting answers you receive with us at the *from you to me* website to let other people read about these fascinating insights . . .

If you liked the concept of this book, please tell your family and friends and look out for others in the *from you to me* range:

Dear Mum, from you to me
Dear Grandma, from you to me
Dear Grandad, from you to me
Dear Sister, from you to me
Dear Brother, from you to me
Dear Son, from you to me
Dear Daughter, from you to me
Dear Friend, from you to me

Cooking up Memories, from you to me
These were the days, from you to me
Christmas Present, Christmas Past, from you to me

other relationship and memory journals available soon . . .